Feet, Head... Go to Bed

Time for bed!

Because falling asleep doesn't have to be hard.

Written by Amy Haworth

Illustrated by Emma Coll

Book design by
Emma Coll

ISBN: 978-1-7364402-0-9

NOBODY MAKES IT ALONE
www.nobodymakesitalone.com

To the special little boy who made me his mom:
I will forever treasure our
" Feet, Head" moments and
promise to always be here for you.
-Mama

At Patrick's home 'round seven o'clock, it was time for calm, but he wanted to rock.

Dinner was over. The sun dipped
low in the sky.
They'd finished pirate battles and
captured bad guys.

A sweet little boy, tired moments ago,
Now had things to do and facts to know.

He began to run. Then laugh. Then play.
And his mommy kept saying, "Put that away."

He brushed his teeth...

...and tried to lay still.
He said he was hot, then
felt a chill.

The lights went off. His eyes opened wide. "I can't fall asleep" he said, as he turned on his side.

Yes, my child. Oh, I know!
"Let's try something new. Let's
give this a go."

She strained to be patient, yet she was beat,
"Really. I promise. This will be neat."

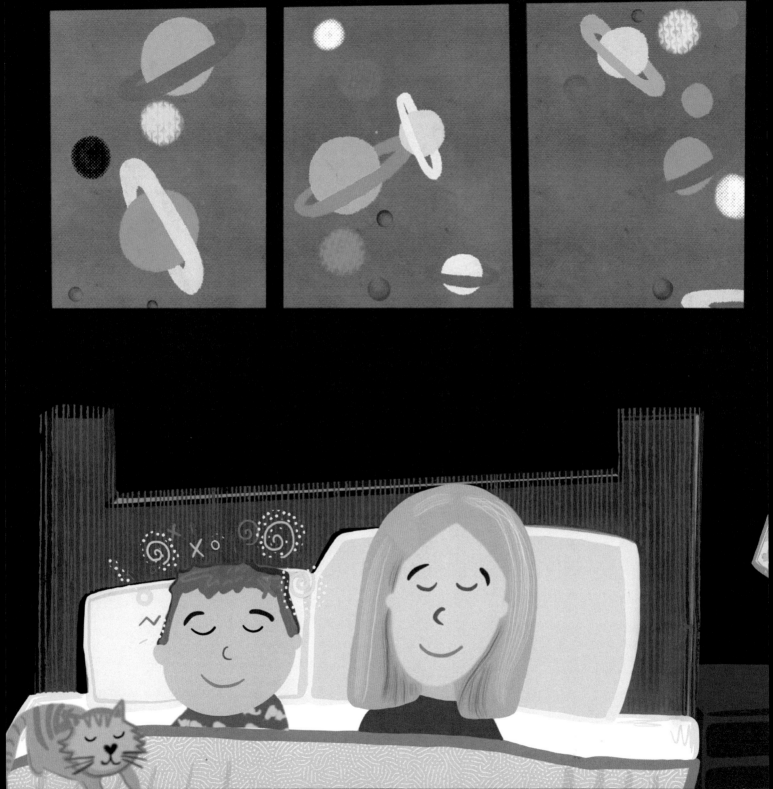

"Listen closely and shut your eyes.
Follow my voice and sleep will arise."

"Breathe in your day and then breathe it out. Bring in the good and release any doubt."

"Listen to the sounds around you now.
The whirr of the fan, and a distant meow."

"Against your skin, you feel the love. Angels surround and protect from above."

"Their love comes in and fills you up,
Into your toes, like they're a cup."

"Your toes fill and grow heavy,
and can't keep it in,
the love overflows and travels within."

"Into the soles of your feet then up through
your calf,
your muscles grow heavy, and it's not
even half."

"Now to your tummy,
you sink deep in bed.
Your arms feel like rocks,
Then we're to your head."

"From the back of your hair to your
nose and your lips,
you're covered in heaviness, it melts
you in drips."

She hugged him and cuddled a little
bit more.
She studied his face then snuck
towards the door.

Life moved so fast, and there was so much to do.
Yet she stopped and she whispered,
"I'm here for you."

"You are kind. You are brave. And, oh, you are strong.
Seize the gift of your life, and may it last long."

The End

...ZZZZZZZZZZZ...

The path to sleep...

Use these words to help your child relax and fall asleep. Use a slow, gentle tone. In most cases, and especially as your child gets used to this nightly routine, your child will fall asleep before you complete the meditation. (You might too!) It's a simple body scan meditation, and we encourage you to experiment with your own words and metaphors to bring relaxation to your child. A recorded example can be found at www.NobodyMakesItAlone.com.

"Take a deep breath in, and with it, bring in your day -- the good, the bad, the events and the activities.
Release your breath and everything from today.
Breathe in your day, and breathe it out.
One more time, get everything from today in that breath... and then let it go.

Outside the angels surround our home. If you listen closely you can hear them singing songs of joy and love.
Their songs weave a force-field to protect you while you sleep.

As they sing, a white light emerges and it gives you peace as it enters your room.
Its warm light is full of love and it enters through your head and moves all the way to your toes,
warming you, comforting you, relaxing you.

It starts to fill your big toes first. Your big toes relax and they get heavier and heavier.
Soon they're full of the light and the love and it spills over to fill the next toe,
then the next, and the next and finally to your baby toe.

The feeling moves to the bottoms of your feet. Through the arch of your foot.
All those steps you've taken today disappear as the warmth builds and moves like honey up to your heel.

Your heel relaxes and then it continues up to your ankle. Your achilles, at the back of your foot, connecting to your calf, relaxes.

Then, inch by inch, the warm, white light relaxes your calves. Little by little, inch by inch, it moves up your leg toward your knee. When it reaches your knee, it refreshes all the springy material that cushions you when you run and jump and play. Your knee soaks it in and is renewed for tomorrow.

Then, inch by inch, the feeling moves to your strong leg muscles, called quadriceps. These are your power source for running and walking. As the light reaches these muscles they relax and grow heavy, and almost half of you now melts into your bed.

Slowly the feeling moves through your bottom, and then it's to your waist. Your breathing is slow, as inch by inch, the feeling moves through your tummy and into your lungs. You notice your lungs feel like balloons as you breathe in deeply -- and slowly breathe out.

From your lungs, the deep feeling of peace and heaviness reaches your heart. You feel it beat and slow as you prepare your body to rest and refresh.

Over your chest and into your collarbone. Then, inch by inch, to your shoulders. Your shoulders relax and the warmth moves down your arms. Past your biceps and then to your elbows. Your elbows sink and melt into the bed. Then, like honey, the relaxation moves into your forearms, to your wrists, and into your hands.

The palms of your hands grow heavy. Then the thumb sinks into the bed.
Followed by your pointer finger, your middle finger, your ring finger, and then your pinky.
All of your fingers and your thumbs are now heavy and full of relaxation.

Your neck gets heavy and the warmth travels up your neck towards your head.
From the back of your head, through the back of your hair, your scalp tingles in a
pleasant way as it relaxes.

The hair takes a break and falls, heavy against your pillow. Over the top of your head the relaxation
travels, past your forehead, down your nose, sweeping your cheeks, and to your lips it goes.

Your jaw opens just a little bit and even your tongue feels heavy. Your eyelids feel like
comfy blankets on your eyes, and your eyebrows sink deeply. Your ears now feel heavy too. They are
closing down for the night and they feel a sense of deep peace that comes from being done for the day.
Your earlobes melt...drooping, melting, slow.

Your whole body now rests, heavy, peaceful.
Every muscle relaxed.
Every cell of your being covered in love.

You are kind, you are brave, and you are strong.

I love you. Unconditionally. Forever."

Amy Haworth and Emma Coll are friends who have partnered in work and life. Together, with other mindful colleagues, they introduced and support a workplace mindfulness program at a global technology company.

They are passionate about sharing how the practice of being present enhances the experience of life. And in that spirit, they worked together to bring this book to parents, caregivers, and children looking for a solution to find sleep.

Amy is a working mom and leadership coach who loves to encourage people to live from their strengths. You can find more of her writing at
Nobody Makes It Alone
www.nobodymakesitalone.com.

Emma is an optimist at heart who centers herself with creativity and mindfulness. She often seeks fleeting inspiration and passes on her favorite quotes and life lessons through art on her @mindful.mins Instagram.

Made in the USA
Las Vegas, NV
11 February 2021